IF I WERE In CHARGE of CHRISTMAS

D0784858

WRITTEN BY HELEN BUCKLEY
ILLUSTRATED BY JENNY BRAKE

But you, Bethlehem Ephrathah,

though you are small among the clans of Judah,

out of you will come for me

one who will be ruler over Israel,

whose origins are from of old,

from ancient times.

MICAH 5:2

If I were in charge
of the first Christmas...
Well, things would have
been very different.

If I were in charge of
Christmas... Hmm...
Let's see...

I'd like pretty things please.
Soft lights.
Nice colours.

I'd like matching shepherds please.
All neat and tidy.

I'd like animals all behaving please.

No mess.
No fuss.

I'd like a smartly wrapped baby please.
All rosy cheeked and snuggly.

If I were in charge of the first Christmas...
Well, things would have been very different.

Jesus being born is too important.

God's Son coming into the world is too precious.

God was in charge of the first Christmas.
He did it just right.

Just as He said He would.
He gave us exactly what we need.

Long, long, long ago

PROMISE

God made His people a promise.
He promised to send His Forever King.

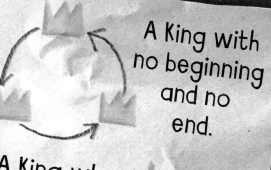

A King with no beginning and no end.

A King who would love and care.

A King who would rescue.

What a promise. What a King!

The King would be given to...

A princess
please?
No.

A prime
minister?
No.

Then at least
a film star?
No.

God is in charge of Christmas.
He did it just right. Just as He said He would.
He gave us exactly what we need.

King Jesus was given to Mary.
Young Mary.
Small and unimportant Mary.

What a God!
He is very great.
He always keeps His promises.

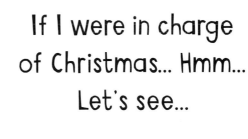

If I were in charge
of Christmas... Hmm...
Let's see...

The King would be born in...

London please? No.

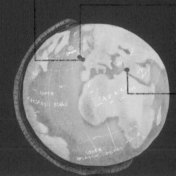

God is in charge of
Christmas. He did it just right.

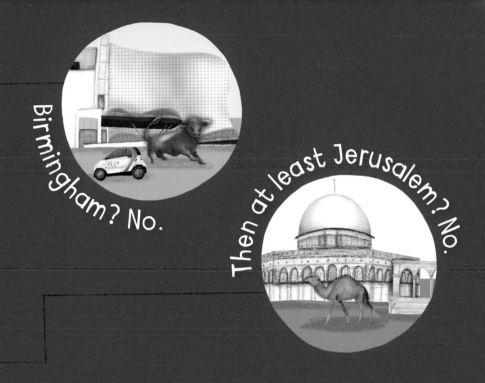

Birmingham? No.

Then at least Jerusalem? No.

And just as He said He would.
He gave us exactly what we need.

King Jesus was born in Bethlehem.
Little old Bethlehem.
Small and unimportant Bethlehem.

What a God!
He is very great.
He always keeps His promises.

If I were in charge of Christmas... Hmm...
Let's see...

The King
would be laid in...

A Moses basket
please? No.

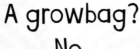

A growbag?
No.

Then at least
a travel cot?
No.

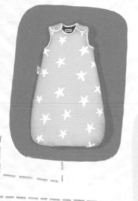

God is in charge of Christmas.
He did it just right.
And just as He said He would.
He gave us exactly what we need.

King Jesus was laid in a manger.
An animal food box.
Small and unimportant.

What a God!
He is very great.
He always keeps His promises.

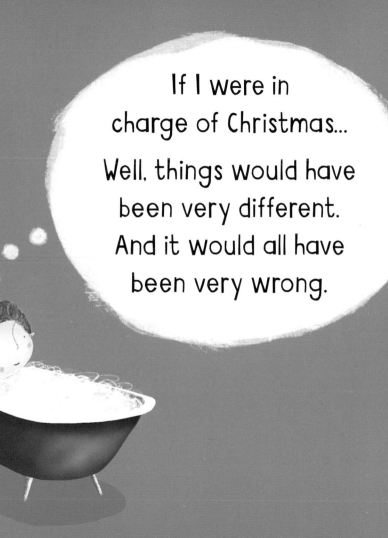

After all... Jesus being born is too important.

God's Son coming into the world is too precious.

God is in charge of Christmas.
He did it just right.

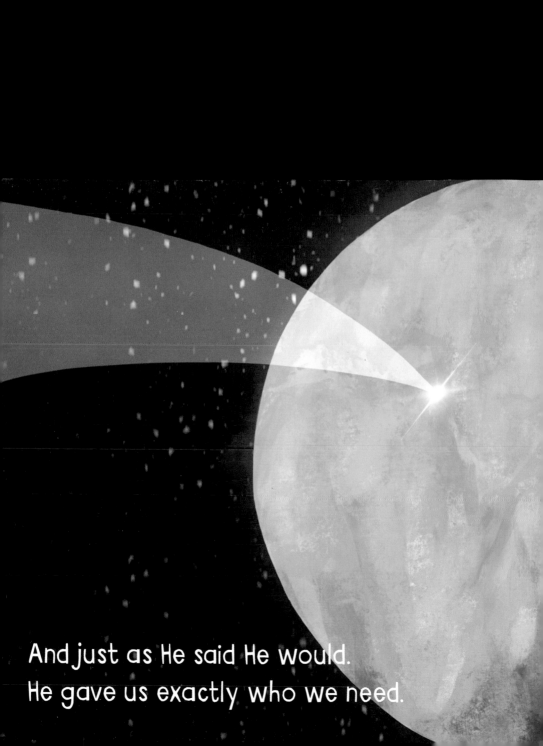

And just as He said He would.
He gave us exactly who we need.

King Jesus is exactly who we need.

The Forever King who loves and cares.

The Forever King who rescues.

Jesus did just the right rescue
so that we can be friends with God.

He did exactly what we need.

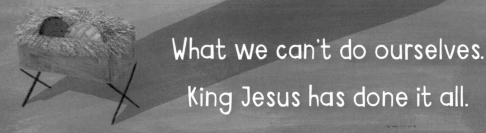

What we can't do ourselves.

King Jesus has done it all.

For Mum and Dad who gave us lovely Christmases.

If I were in Charge of Christmas
Text and Illustrations © 2017 Helen Buckley and Jenny Brake.

Published by 10Publishing, a division of 10ofThose Limited.
ISBN 978-1-911272-74-8

Typeset by Diane Warnes. Printed in Turkey.

10ofThose Limited, Unit C Tomlinson Road, Leyland, PR25 2DY
Email: info@10ofthose.com   Website: www.10ofthose.com

10 Publishing
a division of 10 ofthose.com